Finger Fun
Action Rhyn

Traditional rhymes

Illustrated by Petra Röhr-Rouéndaal

Contents

Five fat sausages

Five fat sausages frying in a pan,
All of a sudden, one went BANG!

Four fat sausages frying in a pan,
All of a sudden, one went BANG!

Three fat sausages frying in a pan,
All of a sudden, one went BANG!

Two fat sausages frying in a pan,
All of a sudden, one went BANG!

One fat sausage frying in a pan,
All of a sudden, it went BANG!

There were no fat sausages frying
in the pan!

3

Incy Wincy Spider

Incy Wincy Spider
Climbed up the spout,
Down came the rain
And washed the spider out.

Out came the sun
And dried up all the rain,
So Incy Wincy Spider
Climbed up the spout again.

Two fat gentlemen

Two fat gentlemen met in a lane,

Bowed most politely, bowed once again.

How do you do? How do you do?

How do you do again?

Two thin ladies met in a lane,

Bowed most politely, bowed once again.

How do you do? How do you do?

How do you do again?

Two tall policemen met in a lane,

Bowed most politely, bowed once again.

How do you do? How do you do?

How do you do again?

Two schoolchildren met in a lane,

Bowed most politely, bowed once again.

How do you do? How do you do?

How do you do again?

Two little babies met in a lane,

Bowed most politely, bowed once again.

How do you do? How do you do?

How do you do again?

Ten little fingers

I have ten little fingers which all
  belong to me,
I can make them do things,
Would you like to see?
I can shut them up tight,
Or open them wide,
Put them all together,
Or make them all hide.
I can lift them up high,
I can put them down low.
I can fold them quietly,
And hold them all just so.

9

Here are Grandma's spectacles

Here are Grandma's spectacles,

And here is Grandma's hat,

And here's the way she folds her hands

And puts them in her lap.

Here are Grandpa's spectacles,

And here is Grandpa's hat,

And here's the way he folds his arms

And puts them in his lap.

11

I'm a little teapot

I'm a little teapot, short and stout,

Here's my handle,

Here's my spout.

When I get the steam up, hear
  me shout,

"Tip me up and pour me out!"

This little bird

This little bird flaps its wings,
Flaps its wings, flaps its wings,
This little bird flaps its wings,
And flies away in the morning.

Ten little people

Ten little people standing straight,

Ten little people open the gate.

Ten little people all in a ring,

Ten little people bow to the king.

Ten little people dance all day,

Ten little people hide away!

Cobbler, cobbler

Cobbler, cobbler, mend my shoe,

Get it done by half-past two.

Look, my toe is peeping through,

Cobbler, cobbler, mend my shoe!